This book is dedicated to my two grandchildren Ellie and Greg
who brought out the child in me. They are buzzing with life and
I enjoy reading poems and stories to them. I became inspired to write this,
my first book, during our many visits to the walled garden in Belvedere House to
watch the honeybees hard at work on the masses of beautiful flowers.
I used my paintings of flowers and bees to illustrate the book.
This was a great learning experience for me.

I am grateful to Belvedere House Gardens & Park, Mullingar.
www.belvedere-house.ie

Belvedere Bee Breeding Group

Lucy Tormey Visual Arts.
www.lucytormeyvisualarts.com

And Particularly
My family and my wonderful friends

Without their support and encouragement
this project would not have been possible.

Published by Mindsi
Design & Print by Mindsi Graphic Design Limited,
23 Martinstown Park, Martinstown, Mullingar, Co. Westmeath, Ireland.
www.mindsi.ie

ISBN: 978-0-9562616-0-1

To Akcia
O Madeline
B Happy
Dolores

If I were a bee

Written & Illustrated by Dolores Keaveney
Email: d_keaveney@yahoo.co.uk

If I were a bee I'd dance on the Sunflowers, their big yellow faces as bright as the sun, hopping and twirling and buzzing for hours, in those big bright flowers I would have so much fun.

If I were a bee I would fly to a poppyfield,

Full of big bright red poppies for miles and for miles,
I would drink all the nectar
I could fit in my tummy,

From those big bright red poppies

with those big bright red smiles.

If I were a bee
I would fly to a meadow,
to collect up some nectar from
each beautiful flower,

I would turn it to honey
in my hive, just one taste
would bring you alive.

If I were a bee I would live
in a beehive,
my brothers and sisters would
all live there too.

We would work very hard making
combs for our honey,

to bring big jars of goodness
to each one of you.

If I were a bee
I would work for hours,
in and out of
the garden
flowers,

The foxgloves,
daisies and
sweet pea too,
collecting up pollen
to make honey
for you.

If I were a bee I
would buzz around
the foxgloves,

I would have so much
fun in and out of each
flower, those pretty
pink foxgloves give
their pollen with
love.

their
pretty pink flowers
fit me like a glove,

If I were a bee I would fly with my friends,

drinking nectar and pollen from each of the flowers.

These big bright red tulips are a sight to behold.

to a bed of **red tulips** so **big** and so **bold**,

If I were a bee I would call on a fuchsia, its big bright flowers would welcome me in,

I would feed on its nectar until I was bursting, thank you dear fuchsia, I will call again.

If I were a bee I would play in an apple tree, with my brothers and sisters I would have so much fun, we would spend all day pollinating the blossoms, so you can have apples kissed by the sun.

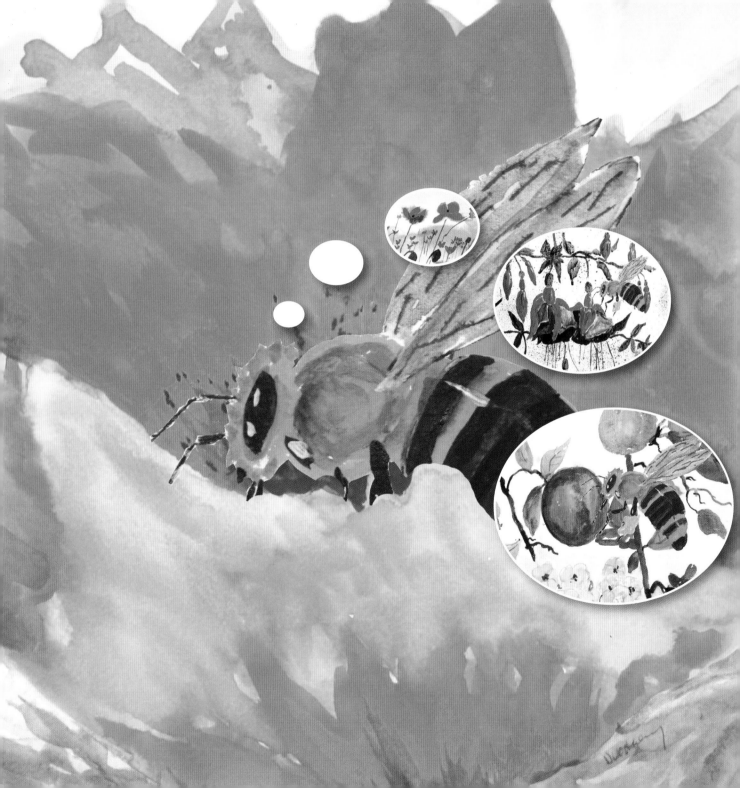

If I were a bee I would sleep in a POPPY,

it's big bright red petals would cuddle me in,

I would dream of new places to work and to play,

and wake in the morning to a sun shining new day.

If I were a bee I would fly to the clouds,

I would twirl and buzz and feel very free,

I would fly to the meadows and flowers and trees,

I could do all these things
If I were a bee.